Silver Burdett Ginn Science

DISCOVERYWORKS

WORKBOOK

LESSON REVIEWS

Silver Burdett Ginn
PARSIPPANY, NJ   NEEDHAM, MA
Atlanta, GA   Deerfield, IL   Irving, TX   Santa Clara, CA

Silver Burdett Ginn
A Division of Simon & Schuster
299 Jefferson Road, P.O. Box 480
Parsippany, NJ 07054-0480

ISBN 0-382-38865-8

4 5 6 7 8 9 10 BW 05 04 03 02 01 00 99 98 97

CONTENTS

UNIT A
INTERACTIONS OF LIVING THINGS 5

UNIT B
LIGHT AND COLOR 17

UNIT C
EARTH THROUGH TIME 29

UNIT D
SOLIDS, LIQUIDS, AND GASES 41

UNIT E
WHAT MAKES ME SICK 53

UNIT A

INTERACTIONS OF LIVING THINGS

Lesson 1
Investigating Living and Nonliving Things 6

Lesson 2
Investigating Needs of Living Things 7

Lesson 3
Investigating Plant Parts 8

Lesson 4
Investigating Resources in the Environment 9

Lesson 5
Investigating Animal Shelters 10

Lesson 6
Investigating Animal Body Parts 11

Lesson 7
Investigating Animals Changing the Environment 12

Lesson 8
Investigating Other Environmental Changes 13

Lesson 9
Investigating Desert Plants and Animals 14

Lesson 10
Investigating Comparing Environments 15

Name_____

1. Ring the pictures of living and once-living things.

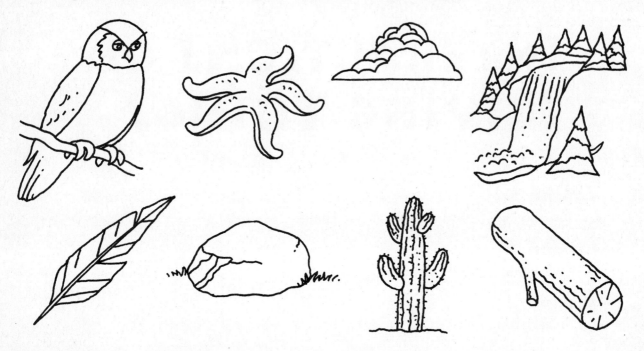

2. Draw four nonliving things you might see at the seashore.

Answers on
Teacher Resource Book p. A54

Name_____

1. Ring the plants and animals that might live in this desert.

2. Look at the picture of the desert habitat. What do the plants and animals need to live?

_____

_____

Name_____

1. Draw a picture of the three main parts of a plant. Then write the name of each part next to it.

2. Write the name of the plant part next to the description of what it does.

What the Plant Part Does	Plant Part
Carries water and nutrients to other parts of the plant	
Makes food for the plant to use	
Holds the plant in the soil and takes in water and nutrients from the soil	

Answers on
Teacher Resource Book p. A54

Name_____

1. Ring the plants and animals that live in a swamp.

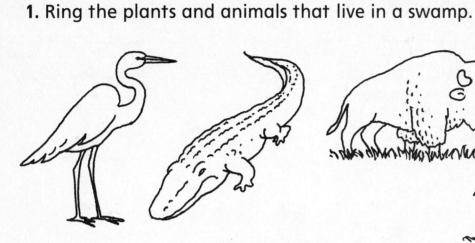

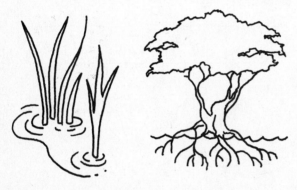

2. How does a turtle use living and nonliving things in a swamp to help it live?

_____

_____

_____

_____

_____

_____

© Silver Burdett Ginn

Answers on
Teacher Resource Book p. A54

Name_____

1. What things does a badger use to make its home?

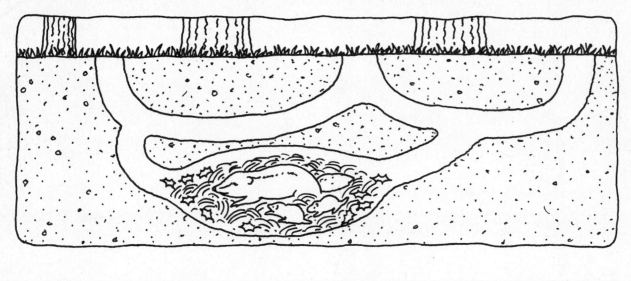

_____

_____

2. What things does an osprey use to make its home?

_____

_____

_____

_____

_____

Answers on
Teacher Resource Book p. A55

Name_____

1. Draw lines to match each bird's beak to the way the bird eats.

Spears fish and other water animals

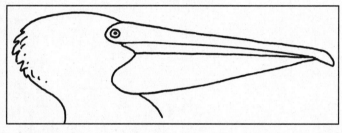

Cracks seeds

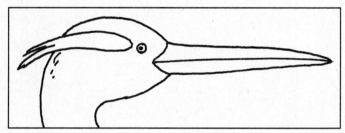

Scoops up fish

2. What body parts help an anteater to get food?

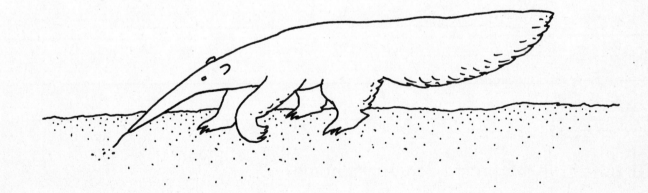

_____

_____

Answers on
Teacher Resource Book p. A55

Name_____

1. How do prairie dogs change the land?

Grasslands

Grasslands With a
Prairie Dog Town

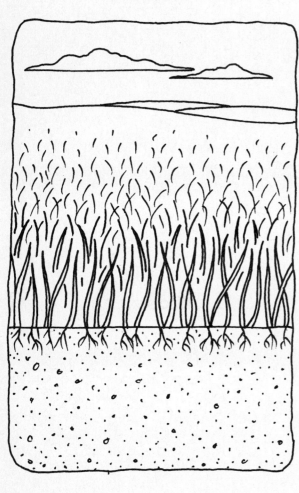

_____

_____

2. How does a prairie dog use its home?

_____

_____

Answers on
Teacher Resource Book p. A55

Name_____

1. How can people change a beach? Is the change helpful or harmful?

_____

_____

_____

2. Put an X on the picture showing change caused by people.

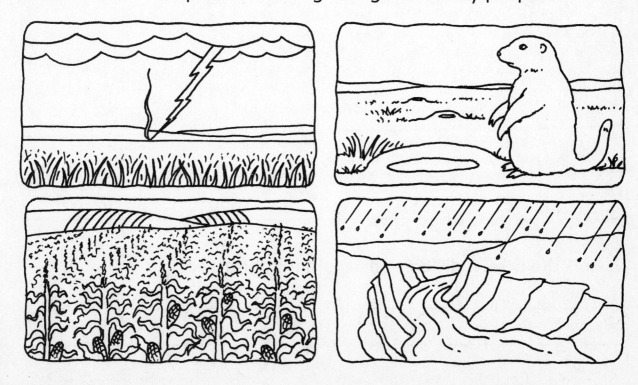

Name_____

1. Draw a picture of a desert. Label each plant and animal in your picture.

2. How are deserts different from other habitats?

_____

_____

Answers on
Teacher Resource Book p. A56

Name_____

1. What body parts help a tiger shark live in the ocean?

_____

_____

_____

_____

_____

2. How is the stem of a water lily different from the stem of a dandelion?

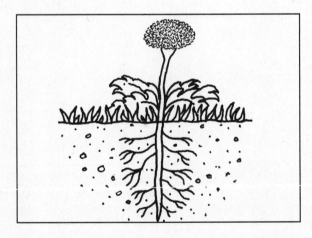 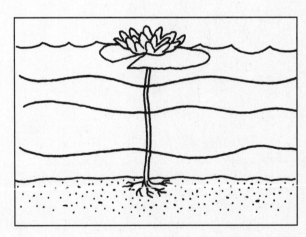

_____

3. How does the stem of a water lily help it to live in a pond?

_____

_____

© Silver Burdett Ginn

LIGHT AND COLOR

Lesson 1
Investigating Light Sources 18

Lesson 2
Investigating How Light Affects What We See 19

Lesson 3
Investigating Objects That Give Off Light and Heat 20

Lesson 4
Investigating How Light Travels in a Straight Line 21

Lesson 5
Investigating How Different Objects Transmit Light 22

Lesson 6
Investigating the Formation of Shadows .23

Lesson 7
Investigating How Shadows Change 24

Lesson 8
Investigating the Separation of White Light into the Spectrum 25

Lesson 9
Investigating the Mixing of Colors 26

Name_____

1. Ring the objects that are light sources.

2. Write the names of the light sources that are natural.

_____

3. Name our most important source of light.

_____

Answers on
Teacher Resource Book p. B53

Name_____

1. Make an *X* on the best place to sit to read a book. Explain why you chose that place.

_____

_____

2. Ring the car on which the license plate would be easier to read.

Answers on
Teacher Resource Book p. B53

Name_____

1. Ring the objects that give off both light and heat.

2. Ring the light source that gives off more heat.

Answers on
Teacher Resource Book p. B53

Name_____

1. Draw a flashlight and show its beam of light hitting the blocks.

2. Ring the line that shows the path of a beam of light.

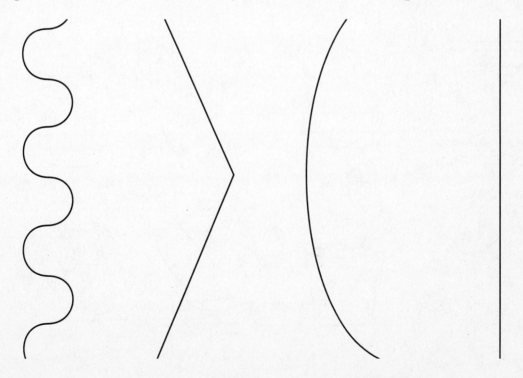

Name_____

1. Ring the bag that lets you see the sandwich most clearly.
   Explain why.

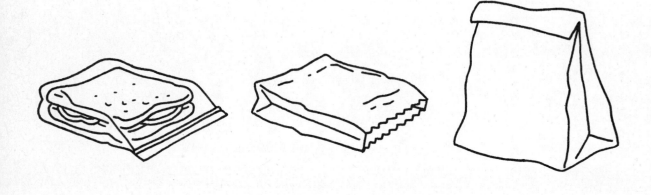

_____

_____

_____

2. Ring the things that do not let any light pass through them.

Answers on
Teacher Resource Book p. B54

© Silver Burdett Ginn

Name_____

1. Match the children's heads to the shadows they make.

2. Ring the objects that would make a round shadow.

Name_____

1. Draw a sun in each of the pictures.

2. Draw the shadow of the mailbox.

© Silver Burdett Ginn

Answers on
Teacher Resource Book p. B54

Name_____

1. Draw the things needed to create a rainbow.

2. Draw a picture of a rainbow. Show all the colors of the spectrum in order.

© Silver Burdett Ginn

Name_____

1. Draw lines from the frog and the kite to the colors that you would mix to paint them.

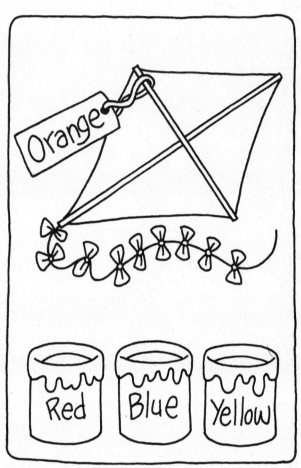

2. Write the names of the colors that you would mix to paint the flowers purple.

_____

Answers on
Teacher Resource Book p. B55

EARTH THROUGH TIME

Lesson 1
Investigating Characteristics of Dinosaurs 30

Lesson 2
Investigating Sizes of Dinosaurs 31

Lesson 3
Investigating Kinds of Fossils 32

Lesson 4
Investigating Imprints 33

Lesson 5
Investigating Handprints and Footprints 34

Lesson 6
Investigating Fossil Remains 35

Lesson 7
Investigating Kinds of Teeth 36

Lesson 8
Investigating Dinosaur Skeletons 37

Lesson 9
Investigating Dinosaurs and Living Animals 38

Name_____

1. Barosaurus and Allosaurus were both dinosaurs. How were they different?

Barosaurus

Allosaurus

_____

_____

_____

2. Ring the sentence that is true.

   A. All dinosaurs had four legs.

   B. Some dinosaurs could fly; some lived in the sea.

   C. Dinosaurs were animals that lived on land a long time ago.

Answers on
Teacher Resource Book p. C57

Name_____

1. Write the name of the biggest dinosaur and the name of the smallest dinosaur.

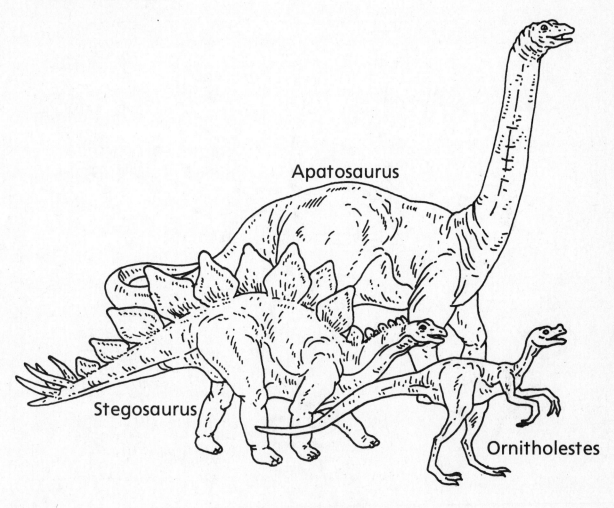

Apatosaurus

Stegosaurus

Ornitholestes

Biggest: _____

Smallest:_____

2. Ornitholestes was about 6 ½ feet long. How does its length compare to the length of your classroom?

_____

_____

Name_____

1. Ring the drawings that show fossil imprints. Put an X on the drawings that show fossil remains.

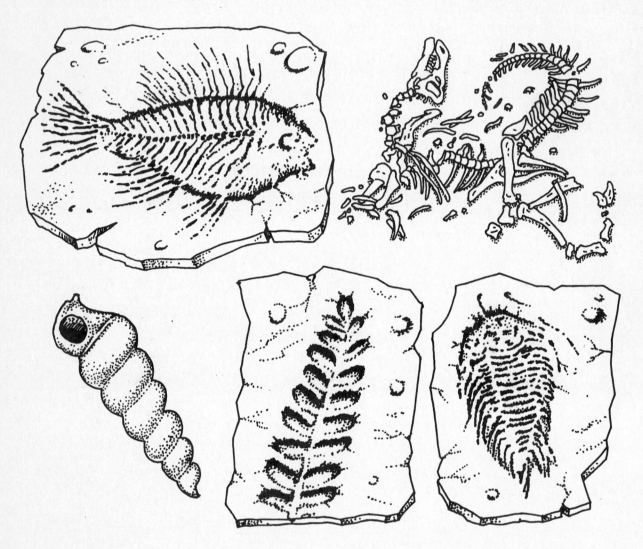

2. Why might it be difficult for scientists to tell what an animal looked like from its remains?

_____

_____

Answers on
Teacher Resource Book p. C57

Name_____

1. How is the fossil imprint of a dinosaur's foot different from a footprint that was just made on a sandy beach?

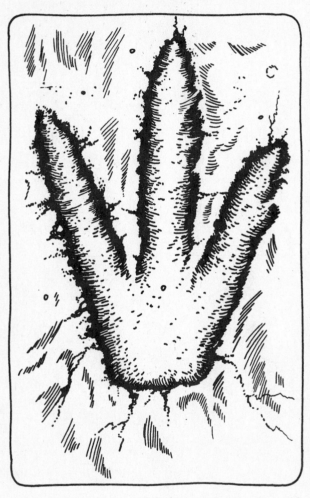 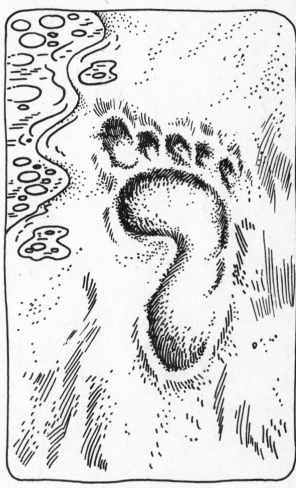

_____

_____

_____

2. What can you learn about an animal by studying its footprint?

_____

_____

© Silver Burdett Ginn

Answers on
Teacher Resource Book p. C57

Name _____

1. Draw a picture of what this dinosaur's footprint might look like.

2. What can you learn about a dinosaur from its fossilized footprint?

_____

_____

_____

_____

Answers on
Teacher Resource Book p. C58

Name_____

1. Look at the skulls. Then match each skull with the dinosaur it comes from.

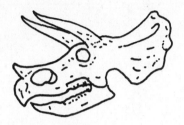

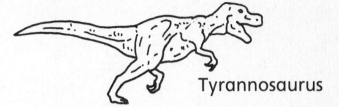

Tyrannosaurus

Triceratops

Lambeosaurus

2. The neck bones of this dinosaur are about 20 feet long. What can you tell about the size of this dinosaur by looking at its neck bones?

_____

_____

Skull and neck bones
of Diplodocus

Answers on
Teacher Resource Book p. C58

Name_____

1. Draw a picture of the teeth of a plant-eating dinosaur. Then draw a picture of the teeth of a meat-eating dinosaur. Label each picture.

2. What kind of food do you
think this dinosaur ate?

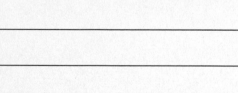

_____

_____

_____

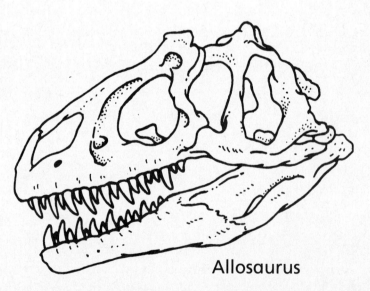

Allosaurus

Answers on
Teacher Resource Book p. C58

Name_____

1. Look at this dinosaur skeleton. What can you tell about the shape of the dinosaur's body?

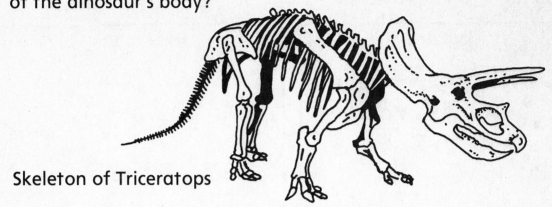

Skeleton of Triceratops

_____

_____

2. Use a crayon or marker to outline the dinosaur skeleton. Then explain what you can tell about the dinosaur's neck and tail from its skeleton.

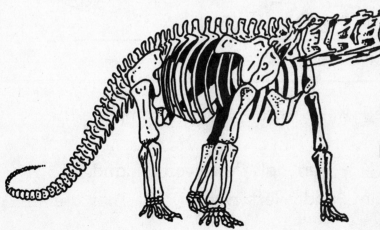

Skeleton of
Mamenchaur

_____

_____

© Silver Burdett Ginn

Name_____

1. What could happen to these endangered animals if they and their habitats are not protected?

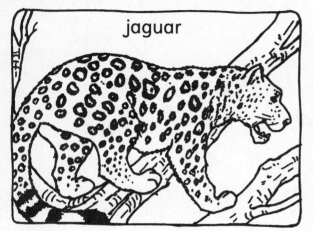
jaguar

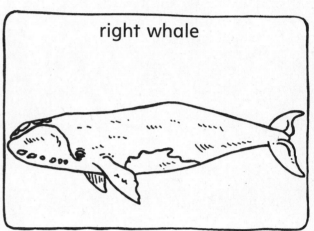
right whale

spider monkey

California condor

sea turtle

_____

2. Use the word <u>endangered</u> or the word <u>extinct</u> to complete the sentences.

   A. Dinosaurs are _____ animals that lived on land.

   B. There aren't many Giant Pandas left in the world. They are _____ animals.

   C. When an animal becomes _____ , it disappears from the earth.

Answers on
Teacher Resource Book p. C59

SOLIDS, LIQUIDS, AND GASES

Lesson 1
Investigating Properties of Solids 42

Lesson 2
Investigating Properties of Liquids 43

Lesson 3
Investigating Shapes of Solids and Liquids 44

Lesson 4
Investigating Properties of Gases 45

Lesson 5
Investigating Objects that Occupy Space 46

Lesson 6
Investigating How a Solid Changes to a Liquid 47

Lesson 7
Investigating How a Liquid Changes to a Gas 48

Lesson 8
Investigating How a Gas Changes to a Liquid 49

Lesson 9
Investigating How a Liquid Changes to a Solid 50

Lesson 10
Investigating Kinds of Matter 51

Name_____

1. All of these objects are solids. How are all solids alike?

_____

_____

2. Ring the solid objects that have the same shape.

Answers on
Teacher Resource Book p. D54

Name_____

1. There are liquids in all of these containers. How are all liquids alike?

_____

_____

2. How are these two liquids alike? How are they different?

Alike: _____

_____

Different: _____

_____

_____

Answers on
Teacher Resource Book p. D54

Name_____

1. Ring the solids. Then put an *X* on the liquids.

2. How is the shape of a solid different from the shape of a liquid?

_____

_____

3. Name two objects that would change shape if you put them in a bowl.

_____   _____

Answers on
Teacher Resource Book p. D54

Name_____

1. Ring the three objects that contain gases.

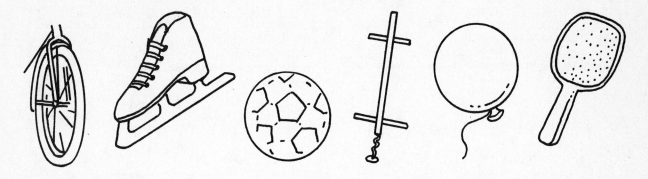

2. Draw pictures that show a balloon before it is blown up and after it is blown up.

Before	After

3. Why does the shape of the balloon change after it is blown up?

_____

_____

© Silver Burdett Ginn

Name_____

1. Name two solids, two liquids, and two gases shown in the picture.

Solids: _____   _____

Liquids: _____   _____

Gases: _____   _____

2. Which objects in the picture take up space?

_____

_____

3. What would happen if you tried to put the pitcher in the same space as the bottle?

_____

_____

Answers on
Teacher Resource Book p. D55

Name_____

1. What will happen to the ice on the pond when winter is over and it becomes much warmer outdoors?

_____

2. Use the words <u>solid</u>, <u>liquid</u>, and <u>water</u> to complete the sentences below.

A. Ice is frozen_____.

B. Water is a_____.

C. Ice is a_____.

Name_____

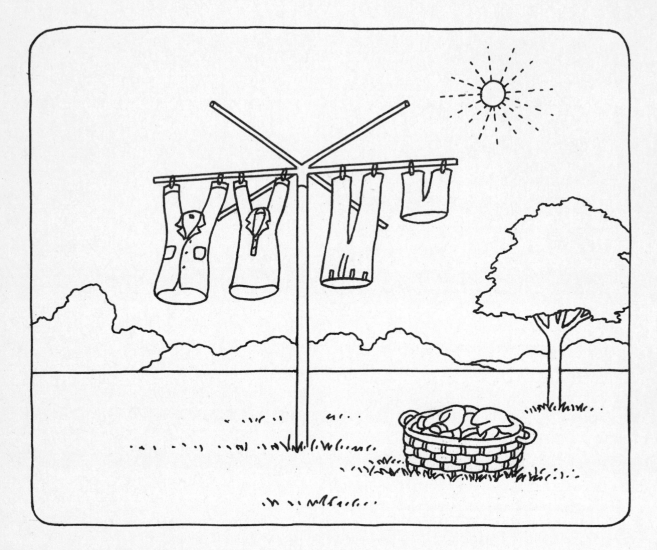

1. What happens to the water in wet clothes when they are hung outdoors on a warm, sunny day?

_____

_____

2. What causes the wet clothes to dry?

_____

_____

Answers on
Teacher Resource Book p. D55

Name_____

1. What happens to the water vapor that evaporates from lakes and rivers?

_____

_____

2. What causes water vapor in the air to change into tiny droplets of water in clouds?

_____

_____

© Silver Burdett Ginn

Name _____

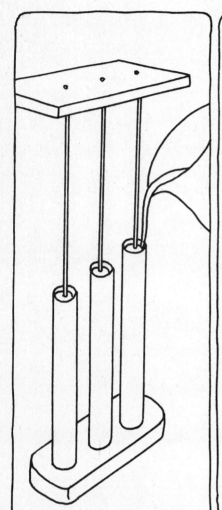
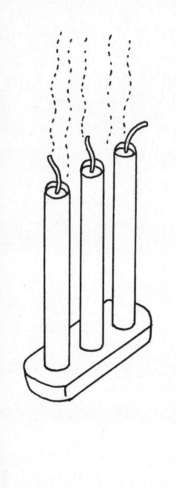
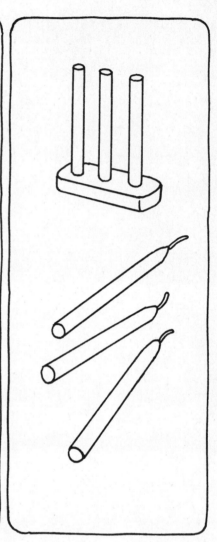

1. When wax candles are made, how does wax change from one state of matter to another?

_____

_____

2. When water turns to ice, how is it changed from a liquid to a solid?

_____

Answers on
Teacher Resource Book p. D56

Name_____

1. Name two solids, two liquids, and two gases shown in the picture.

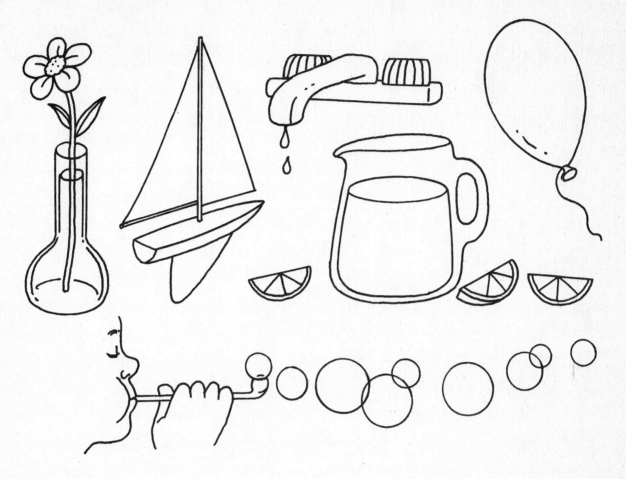

Solids: _____   _____

Liquids: _____   _____

Gases: _____   _____

2. How do you know a bicycle tire is filled with air if you can not see the air?

_____

_____

Answers on
Teacher Resource Book p. D56

UNIT E

WHAT MAKES ME SICK

Lesson 1
Investigating Germs 54

Lesson 2
Investigating How a Sneeze Spreads Germs 55

Lesson 3
Investigating How Germs are Spread 56

Lesson 4
Investigating How Your Body Protects You From Germs 57

Lesson 5
Investigating How to Prevent the Spread of Germs 58

Lesson 6
Investigating How to Prevent Sickness and Injury 59

Lesson 7
Investigating How to Stay Healthy 60

Name_____

1. Describe the shapes of these germs.

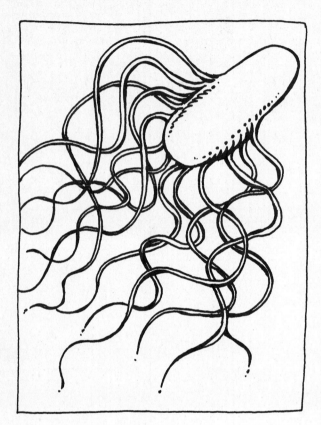

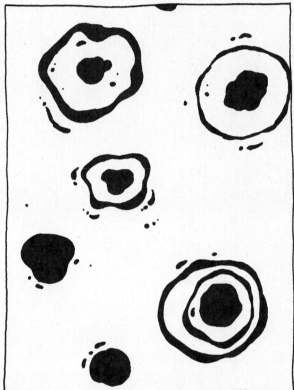

Germ A   Germ B

_____   _____

_____   _____

_____   _____

2. What instrument or tool would you need to use to be able to see germs? Explain why you need help to see germs.

_____

_____

_____

Answers on
Teacher Resource Book p. E47

Name_____

1. How do germs spread when someone sneezes?

_____

_____

2. What can you do to keep germs from spreading when you sneeze?

_____

_____

_____

Name_____

1. Ring three places in this kitchen where you might find germs.

2. Ring places in the picture where germs are being spread. Place an X on places where children are helping to prevent the spread of germs.

© Silver Burdett Ginn

Answers on
Teacher Resource Book p. E47

Name_____

1. How are these people protecting themselves from dust and germs?

_____

_____

_____

_____

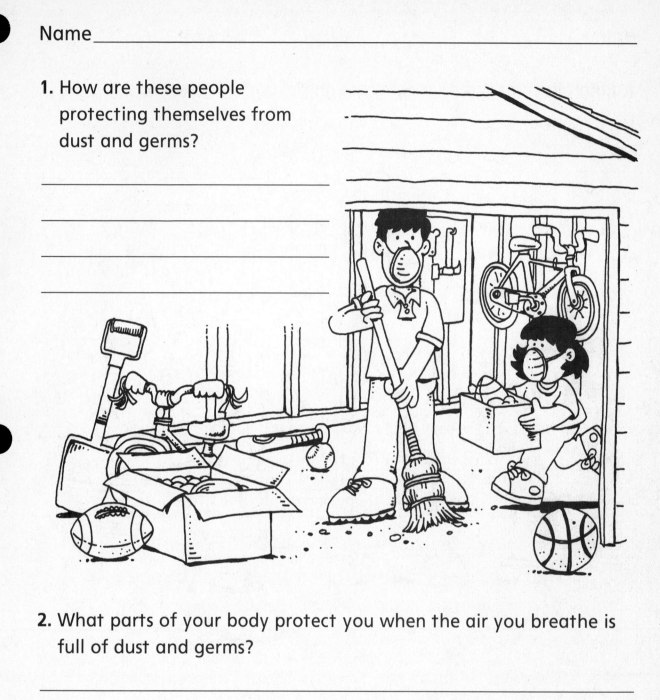

2. What parts of your body protect you when the air you breathe is full of dust and germs?

_____

_____

3. Why are mucous membranes able to trap dust and germs?

_____

_____

Answers on
Teacher Resource Book p. E47

Name_____

1. Ring places in this picture where germs are being spread.

2. What can the children in the pictures do to prevent germs from spreading?

_____

_____

_____

Answers on
Teacher Resource Book p. E48

© Silver Burdett Ginn

Name_____

1. Look at the pictures. How could the injury have been prevented?

_____

_____

_____

2. Ring things the people in each picture are doing to help prevent injuries.

Answers on
Teacher Resource Book p. E48

Name_____

1. Ring the foods that are healthful.

2. Ring the two activities that are harmful.

    A. Swimming without a lifeguard being present

    B. Buckling your seat belt in a car

    C. Using sunscreen lotion when out in the sun

    D. Leaving toys on the stairs

Answers on
Teacher Resource Book p. E48